CW00409269

The day my brain

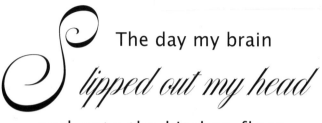
Slipped out my head

and onto the kitchen floor

A journey through psychosis

Melanie Burnell

live it
PUBLISHING

Copyright © 2014 by Melanie Burnell

First published in 2014 by:
Live It Publishing/Britain's Next Bestseller.

An imprint of Live It Ventures Ltd
27 Old Gloucester Road
London, United Kingdom.
WC1N 3AX

www.bnbsbooks.co.uk

The moral right of Melanie Burnell to be identified as the
author of this work has been asserted by her in accordance
with the Copyright, Designs and Patents Act 1988.

All rights reserved.
Except as permitted under current legislation, no part
of this work may be photocopied, stored in a retrieval
system, published, performed in public, adapted, broadcast,
transmitted, recorded or reproduced in any form or by any
means, without the prior permission of the copyright owners.

All enquiries should be addressed to
Britain's Next Bestseller

ISBN: 9781910565070

What Is Psychosis?

Psychosis is a medical word used to describe mental health problems that stop a person from thinking clearly, telling the difference between reality and their imagination, and acting in a normal way - www.nhs.uk

Psychosis is a serious, life threatening illness. It is a term used to describe a group of unusual and distressing thoughts and experiences involving some sort of loss of contact with reality. Psychosis can be experienced by anyone and is most common in young people aged between 14 and 35.

Psychotic Depression is a debilitating mental illness where a person suffers from the dangerous combination of depressed mood and psychosis that, tragically, often ends in suicide. While this condition is completely treatable, thousands of cases remain misdiagnosed or overlooked by mental health professionals due to a lack of awareness of the condition and its symptoms. The same lack of awareness of the illness means that sufferers are unsure of what is happening to them which can be extremely frightening and can lead to unfortunate outcomes.

Based on studies in both an inpatient and outpatient setting, an estimated 16%-54% of depressed adults have psychosis, although it is commonly not diagnosed. The great tragedy is that the illness is treatable if recognised early. Unfortunately the diagnosis is frequently missed, leading to the prescription of ineffective treatments and often tragic outcomes.

"The person with psychotic depression feels an unbearable horror, which greatly increases the risk of suicide for someone with this illness"

- Dr Anthony Rothschild M.D., Professor of Psychiatry

"Psychosis is a neglected problem in psychiatry"

- Paul E. Keck Jr., M.D., Professor of Psychiatry and Neuroscience

Special Note

To my beautiful daughter Riannon. I love you very much. This book is dedicated to you. You make me so proud every time I look at you.

I would like to thank my wonderful family, Riannon, my Mum, my Dad and sister Caz for all your support. Your love helped pull me through, no doubt. I love you all dearly. My Mum did not miss one hospital visit – twice a day for three months she came to see me.

Thank you to my Mum's good friend Margaret and my Auntie Marilyn for supporting my Mum throughout. Thank you to Beatrice from the Early Intervention Team, my wonderful Care Worker. To Ivan, Richard, to the hospital nurses, OT staff, doctors and psychiatrists, Dr Blidge, Dr Bhashir and all the team at SEPT for their support.

Thank you to my good friends Liz, Em, Daren, Jamie and all my other wonderful friends whose good wishes, help and support will never be forgotten. I am blessed to have you all in my life. Your support and friendship is cherished dearly.

I hope this book inspires and educates people. And if it saves just one life it was worth doing.

Melanie x

Chapter One

"Who's McHammer?" My Dad asked innocently, pointing towards a gold framed CD mounted on the wall as we all sat round the table in the Planet Hollywood restaurant in Las Vegas. Immediately myself, my Mum and my little sister all fell about laughing uncontrollably. My Dad looked bewildered.

"Why are you all laughing?" he asked.

"It's M.C. Hammer!" I said and we all laughed some more.

I was fourteen and we had gone to America for a three week family holiday. A typical stroppy teen, life hadn't been a bed of roses for me. A long stint of bullying a few years back in middle school had dented my confidence and I tended to be pretty moody. I grew up fast a few years later when I found myself pregnant at just 19. I moved out of my parent's suburban family home and into a council flat and set up a new life as a young, strong minded and capable single Mum.

With the support of my family I managed well and

my beautiful daughter Riannon grew up quickly before all our eyes. As she approached three years old, I had an idea to paint bespoke artwork to match client's interiors following my Mum's dilemma in which she could not find a suitable modern artwork to hang in her newly decorated kitchen. "I'll paint you one Mum!" I announced, feeling inspired after visiting my little sister's GCSE art show. I'd always been very creative and good at art. My painting of a long stemmed blue flower looked perfect in her room and my entrepreneurial spirit ignited. I enrolled on business courses funded by the Princes Trust and embarked on a 10-year journey which saw me paint collections for wealthy clients and upmarket pub and restaurant chains, represent other artists and eventually run my own art galleries.

My desire to become successful became a formidable driving force and at one stage I represented 200 artists and had 10 staff in an incredible arts centre I had created from scratch. My vision of success was so strong that I kept pushing myself on even though amazingly I never managed to pay myself a wage; my out-goings were always more than my income even though at one stage I was turning over more than £75k a year.

I had learned to live off adrenalin and belief, two very powerful tools it would transpire. My parents helped me out with petrol money and electricity bills and together with the government tax credits I received as a non-earner, somehow I got by. I always believed it would be worth it in the end and the idea of giving up never crossed my mind. I plugged away like someone possessed, unstoppable every day, painting, promoting, running my gallery and in more recent years working through the night developing my complex art gallery website as well.

Life was tough as a single Mum with a demanding business and no money but I knew no different. With the help of copious amounts of coffee, wine and cigarettes I constantly pushed myself to manage my punishing schedule and ever mounting To Do lists with the belief that 'everything will work out' firmly in my mind at all times. While my friends of a similar age were enjoying nice holidays and clothes I got by wearing my sister's hand-me-downs. In 2009 despite being at the height of the recession I partnered up with a business associate who bought into my vision of creating a huge arts centre dedicated to showcasing the artwork of hundreds of emerging artists. I was convinced this was the project that would finally make me successful and I was going to give it everything I had. At the time I was running a smaller gallery and could see the potential of replicating it on a much bigger scale but I knew it would take two of us. I sold her my vision and she too became hooked on my dream of success. We went into partnership and took on the lease of a huge old derelict listed building, one of the oldest in Bedfordshire, and converted it into a thriving arts centre.

I already knew about hard work at this point but had no idea how many inner resources I had until now. I strongly believed I could achieve anything I put my mind to and was focussed on making this a success. I was a go-getter, always had been. Together with a positive outlook and a new business partner I felt I had all the ingredients needed and set to work.

Life was crazy. My alarm would sound at 6am and up I'd get each morning, like Groundhog day, tidy round, get Riannon now 9, to school, do a 10-hour shift at the arts centre, collect Riannon from the child minder or my parents house then go home to cook tea, run her bath and put her to bed, then set to work on my pc or paint (or both!) finally going to bed around 4am, if at all, then the cycle would start all over again.

Days at the centre included interviewing artists and getting them to sign up to exhibition space, hanging their work in our four gallery rooms, creating marketing material, writing newsletters, press releases, running art soiree evenings, arts classes and working on our website.

There was a huge pressure to sign more artists and keep them happy as they rented wall space which we needed to stay afloat. We had to have 40 artists paying to exhibit at any one time, over twice our initial estimation. Of course they expected sales in return and if this didn't happen they needed persuading not to pull out – it was like walking a tight rope every day suspended above leaping flames of fire, just trying not to fall. I would take on more and more creating different events to show the artists we were a busy, vibrant centre with lots of customers to justify their outlay. It never stopped; it was one long wild rollercoaster.

I just held on tight, closed my eyes and went with it believing I would reap the rewards in the end.

Even on Sundays we opened one of the galleries as a family portrait photography studio and bleary eyed I'd go down and be the photographers assistant, making the babies laugh for the camera. I became really good at multitasking and achieved a lot under pressure, never once lacking focus or taking my eye off my goal. I was determined to make a better life for me and my daughter and that this was the way to do it.

It wasn't long before I realised I had created a monster. We ran art workshops, held art lectures, offered a bespoke framing and canvas printing service and stocked work from internationally acclaimed published artists as well as our many local ones. I would often sleep over at the gallery at weekends when Riannon stayed at my parents, sleeping on the sofa in our main first floor gallery. I lived and breathed that centre, hanging and pricing all the work, selling exhibition spaces to artists, designing all our promotional catalogues and leaflets and promoting all our events. My partner focussed on logistics including ordering, stock control, finance and admin.

We achieved a phenomenal amount together and both worked tirelessly.

Our over heads were much higher than we'd anticipated and we realised early on that we would have to take the concept of selling artists exhibition spaces online to stand any chance of making a profit. We hired a web developer and I immersed myself in this project on

top of everything else. The financial pressures to keep the centre going were huge but we were tied into a three year contract. I felt I had an enormous responsibility to my partner, artists and staff to make a success of it as it was my vision they had all bought into in the first place.

Each day my heart would start racing as soon as I set foot in the centre. I'd try to keep everyone motivated and inspired.

"We will make it! It will be worth it!" I'd promise them all. I felt like I'd dragged other people into my crazy world and it was sink or swim. I kept kicking my legs so that my head was just above the water. I made the same promises to Riannon who didn't understand why I worked so much when we still had no money or any kind of decent lifestyle. "It will be worth it, you'll see. I promise." Meanwhile our out-goings were climbing every month and I knew that the complex website I'd been working on was now our only chance of success.

The mental strength, focus and determination required during this time was overwhelming. I invested so much of myself to the detriment of my health and family relationships but I was unstoppable. I hardly ate and hardly slept. The pressure to get the site up and running before our funds ran out was immense. We needed it to work so that we could make the transition from the centre, which was like a noose around our necks, to the freedom our online gallery would give us before our funds ran out and we lost everything.

Time was running out, deadlines came and went and

things finally came to a head when we closed the centre in late December 2011, a year short of our lease end. We had negotiated an early exit with our landlord and our amazing site was finally ready which had cost in excess of £12k, much more than we had anticipated. But it looked great, I had convinced our artists that taking them online was the best step to take and there was relief all round. The site would be our sole focus in the New Year. We had done it! Except I was done in. Really done in. Things had started going downhill in the June prior to closing the centre.

"Something's wrong with my eyes!" I screamed to my Mum. It was a Friday evening and I'd just got back from the gallery to my Mums to collect Riannon. I was looking across the room when suddenly everything split into two – I was literally seeing double! Driving home was horrendous; I could not tell which of the cars on the road were real and which were the double illusion! I went with my Mum to the optician the next day. They tested my eyes. "Well you don't need glasses" he said, "you have perfect vision. I'm concerned there may be a problem behind the eyes." He made an appointment at the hospital. Could it be a tumour? I was worried.

A week later I went to the hospital for tests. "You're fine" the consultant said. I was relieved. "We sometimes see this in people who are very stressed. The muscles behind the eyes weaken. It's temporary."

Well that certainly rang true. I was giving myself pep talks most days just to keep going. "Come on Mel, you can do this, keep going!" I'd say, desperate to push past the tiredness and exhaustion so I could keep up with my huge workload. I was working so many hours and pushing myself so hard it was clearly beginning to take its toll, however I was in no position to change this right now. I had to get the site up and running before the gallery closed at all costs; at any cost. And so I continued with my crusade, my unstoppable mission. I was losing weight and looking strained and my family became increasingly concerned. They begged me to take it easy. "Once the gallery has closed and I've had a rest over Christmas I'll be fine" I'd try to reassure them.

But things just got worse and worse.

My nightmare was just beginning.

My Mum's Record Of What Was Happening

Melanie was working far too hard, becoming irritable and losing weight. She was smoking far too much and looking back this was the beginning of her downward spiral into what we now know was psychosis. In August 2011 both her father and myself knew she had to have a break from her endless routine of sleepless nights and long meetings, so we arranged for her and Riannon to go on holiday to Majorca for a weeks inclusive break, hoping to see a more relaxed daughter on her return.

While she was more relaxed it soon became obvious

she was returning to her manic lifestyle and becoming very stressed again. We begged her to take more time out, work less hours but she didn't listen.

As parents we could see that something would have to give soon. She was changing into a much less confident young woman, always stressed, worried she was going to let people down and caring less about her health.

It was about this time that Melanie met Richard.

Melanie Burnell

Chapter Two

I met Richard in September a month or so before things started getting really bad for me. We just clicked straight away and he was very supportive of my business and plans to take my gallery online. He could see I was close to breaking point and warned I was heading for a 'train crash.' He seemed in awe of the amount I did each day. To me it had become normal but to others looking in it seemed a crazy way to live your life – working to such extreme lengths for no pay. "You really should try to take things a bit more easy" he'd say. "Sure" I'd reply, "once things have moved online I'll do just that." I didn't really have time in my life for a boyfriend but Richard phoned me every day and fitted in with me as much as possible. He brought me sandwiches for lunch so that I didn't miss meals and helped clear things from the gallery as we prepared to wind it down. As things really began to take their toll on me just a few weeks later, he became my rock.

Within a few weeks I began getting very shaky, teary and panicky. I went off my food and felt very overwhelmed a lot of the time even though my workload had all but finished – I'd done all the hard work, now we were just winding the gallery down. This should have been the easy part for me as my PA and business partner took control of selling off our furnishings and arranging artists to collect their work. Unable to hide or control that I was not myself I went to my doctor who diagnosed depression. He put me on anti-depressants.

By November I was a quivering wreck. I spent my days trying to help pack things up at the gallery but I was not really much use. "Try focussing on one task at a time" my business partner and PA advised. They had both had depression in the past. I tried to take their advice but it wasn't any use. My family begged me to go back to the doctors who upped my dose of anti-depressants. By the time the gallery closed just before Christmas 2011 I was a shadow of my former self. My weight had plummeted and I was a wreck.

Richard tried to help me by spending more time at mine after work during the week, helping look after Riannon by getting her packed lunch ready for school, polishing her shoes and ironing her school uniform. At weekends he would take us to his where he would wash all our clothes from the week and encourage me to try to rest. He did so much for me that in our first three months of being together he lost almost three stone in weight.

I was finding things increasingly difficult. I became quiet, withdrawn and nervous. It was a far cry from the super confident, loud and exuberant young woman I was previously. I felt as though my thoughts were not right, like my brain was shutting down. I had trouble thinking straight or following conversations. I was convinced I would never recover and that I was going insane.

I could no longer manage simple tasks like cleaning or straightening my hair. I was barely sleeping at night and would get transfixed by a minor thought which I would focus on for hours at a time for example, why had my business partner not text me back, what was going on? It would take me up to two hours to write a simple text message. I could not string the correct words together. It was so frustrating; previously easy tasks were now a huge problem for me. I felt like I was losing my mind and began over-thinking and worrying about tiny things to the Nth degree – something I had never done before. I used to be so flippant. Now I literally could not have one thought in my head without this happening so I tried to think of nothing. It was indescribably torturous. I felt like I couldn't be trusted to have any thoughts in my head. I could not read the paper or watch the TV in case another thought got 'implanted' in my head. I was unable to relax at all; my heart would race all day and all night.

Everything I imagined became magnified in my mind. It was like living in a dreadful nightmare. I feared I had no control over my thoughts. The veins in my head would bulge and my heart would pound all the time. I was unable to process anything or think straight. It was like my brain had gone haywire and was shutting down. Night times were horrendous. I would pace around and freak out all night.

Richard became obsessed with researching therapies for depression online such as CBT in a quest to get me well again. He would spend many hours 'counselling' me even though he worked in security and had no experience in mental health. He was much older than me and was very over-bearing. I would find these sessions exhausting. I would try to implement the different ways of thinking as well as focus on my positives which were pinned up all over my flat, but I just couldn't make any sense of it and ended up feeling like my brain was overloaded. These sessions could last up to 9 hours. My brain felt frazzled.

Prior to this, I had always been a very creative person. I had always relied heavily on my instincts and visualised everything. If you said you're cooking dinner, I'd picture you in my mind cooking dinner. Reading the menu in a restaurant I'd 'see' the plates of food in my mind. I also associated colours quite randomly and subconsciously to certain words like days of the week, numbers, names and places. I always presumed everyone could do this until one Sunday family dinner a few years ago when I casually mentioned that "Wednesdays are a pinky-red with splashes of orange." My Mum nodded knowingly and informed me that hers were sky blue. Everyone else around the table stared at us like we had two heads. "What are you talking about?!" I've never met anyone else who has this ability other than my Mum although I read on the internet that it's a harmless sense phenomenon called

Synesthesia. Some people see colours when they think of certain words like me, others taste things instead! I always felt blessed that I had this special ability and even painted a collection of artwork depicting my days of the week when I was at college.

At the time of my spiralling depression I realised one day that all my colours had gone. It was a sudden realisation one day that there were no longer familiar colours attached to things any more and there hadn't been for some time. It was such a sad moment when I realised I'd lost my colours. When I told my Mum, I think she knew more than anyone what that represented.

My Mum's Record Of What Was Happening

Melanie was spending weekends at Richards but I felt she wasn't enjoying her time with him and I was beginning to wonder if he was having an effect on her loss of confidence. I really didn't care for him much as I found him a very miserable person and wondered if his moods were helping to bring Melanie down. I realised how bad she had become one Friday in December and it really shocked me.

We were going to Riannon's school Christmas bazaar and had arranged to meet at my house and all go together. Melanie arrived at mine shaking and crying saying she couldn't cope with going to the school fate. I was so shocked. I naively thought she would feel better after having some food and drink; I thought she just hadn't been looking after herself. When Richard arrived we decided to call the Doctor and explain how Melanie was feeling. The GP said he would increase her anti-depressants and we should go to see him the following week. I was scared now that something was really not right with Melanie. As the weeks went on towards Christmas we visited her GP weekly explaining she was now not sleeping or eating and was crying a lot.

Something that was very frightening was seeing the veins on her forehead literally bulging. I saw her not sleeping even with prescribed sleeping tablets and sedatives. I knew she was putting on a brave face at Christmas and I thank her for that but we knew it was not going away.

Whatever 'it' was it was getting worse.

Chapter Three

Christmas came and went and I struggled through even though every day I was quietly going through head explosions and dizziness. It was now January and I wanted so much to get my business back on track. I'd attend meetings with my business partner and web developer but I just couldn't make sense of what was being said. "Come on Mel, I need you," my business partner would say. She would email me minutes of our meetings. I tried so hard to focus but I would just spend hours on the computer not achieving anything.

Richard could see me struggling and tried to help me out by producing fancy promotional videos and impressive QR codes that could be added to the site so that I had something to show at our meetings. However I was finding things impossible. It would take me an hour or more to write a simple email and I became extremely paranoid that my partner and PA were conspiring against me. It turns out this wasn't far from the truth. However, I could spend up to seven hours sat at my kitchen table, head in hands, transfixed on the thought that they were plotting on taking the business away from me and be unable to focus on anything else. I couldn't do any work and the website stagnated. I found this very frustrating but more than that I was getting increasingly desperate about not being able to cope with day to day life.

I hadn't slept properly in months and had lost yet more weight. I was barely functioning at all. Richard continued to 'counsel' me and I continued to shake all day and pace all night like something possessed. I was convinced that I was a terrible person with an incurable mental illness who would be locked up and branded insane. I was petrified. I did not know what was happening or why or how to stop it. Richard bought me sketch pads and pencils to try to get me to draw, something I had always loved to do. But it was like trying to write with the wrong hand, I just couldn't do it. It was so frustrating. My talent for drawing had vanished along with my personality, colours and zest for life.

Mum kept taking me back to the doctors to no avail. He just kept saying the same thing; I had depression and with rest I would get better. In desperation my parents paid for me to see a psychiatrist. I had become terrified that I was going crazy and worried that he would lock me up. I walked into his office with my Mum and Richard. He asked me lots of questions including had I contemplated suicide. The truth? Yes. But I did not want to admit to this in case he locked me away. I had 30 minutes with him and he suggested we try different anti-depressants.

He also prescribed sedation pills and said I should move in with my parents for two weeks and rest. He said not to even attempt to do any work and assured us that in time, I would be OK.

Riannon and I moved into my parent's house and they looked after us. But I still could not sleep or relax. My Mum grew increasingly concerned and made yet another appointment with my doctor. "Her head pounds – you can see the veins in her head bulging and her heart races all the time. She is desperately unwell, please do something," she pleaded. It was true. I would lay with a cold flannel over my forehead trying to relieve the incredible pressure and pulsating veins in my head for hours on end. The doctor diagnosed high anxiety and said I needed to rest. He prescribed anti anxiety anti-depressants, sleeping pills and diazepam. He also referred me for professional counselling. Riannon and I moved back home and I continued to get close support from my Mum and Richard.

I tried to embrace the CBT counselling. I tried to implement the relaxation breathing techniques they taught me along with trying to combat my negative thoughts but nothing worked. After a few sessions they stopped it saying I had to get my anxiety down before they could help me as I was so anxious that I could not concentrate properly. I was so upset – I was trying so hard, but they were right. How could I benefit from the sessions when I could not even retain the information they were giving me?

As time went on thoughts of suicide entered my head

more often. I would be driving along and think "right, I'm going to go to the train station and jump in front of a train." I always thought better of it for Riannon's sake. One time I was meeting my business partner in town and as I waited to cross the busy road I thought about stepping out in front of an oncoming bus. This way I thought people would think it was an accident and wouldn't be hurt by the fact I had intended to kill myself.

At the time Whitney Houston had been reported to have died from an overdose and it was all over the TV. At Richard's house he would have MTV on in the lounge and every time one of her songs came on I thought about joining her. I tried very hard to fight my suicidal thoughts every time I had them but as time went on this became harder to do. It seemed increasingly like the only way out of the nightmare I was stuck in.

My doctor referred me to an NHS psychiatrist who asked many of the same questions as the previous one. Again, I did not want to admit to feeling suicidal for fear I would be locked up but I did pluck up the courage to tell him. He just echoed what the other psychiatrist and doctor had said, that I should continue with my anti-depressants and rest.

My Mum's Record Of What Was Happening

By early January I was finding seeing Melanie getting

worse and her GP telling me it was 'just anxiety' and that she only needed to rest too much to cope with and one morning at work I broke down and cried. For the first time I had spoken about this dreadful condition Melanie had to someone. That person was my Manager and she told me her sister had had a 'breakdown' and was now fine and that she knew exactly what I was feeling. I found this very comforting. I then made the decision that Melanie should see a psychiatrist. As I worked in a private hospital I had access to one who I shared my concerns with. He arranged to see her a couple of days later but said I would need a doctor's referral.

Melanie and I went to see her GP the next day explaining we wanted a letter of referral to a psychiatrist. "Why don't you just see one on the NHS?" he asked. When I asked how long the wait would be he said six weeks! I couldn't contain my anger as I told him my daughter was getting more ill daily and couldn't wait that long. He put in Melanie's referral letter that 'Melanie's mother is so anxious it's making Melanie's anxiety worse.' I really worried that he was taking our cries for help so flippantly and had no idea just how ill she was becoming but had faith that seeing a psychiatrist would make her better. How wrong I was.

As more tablets were prescribed, I clung to the hope that these were the ones to make her better. What I saw was my daughter getting worse. When she came to stay with me for her two weeks 'rest,' I saw that she was now unable to do very much for herself. I saw with my own eyes how she paced the floor all night and how she craved to drink water all through the night like it was a ritual. She would get into bed and a couple of minutes later get out to get water. This pattern would be repeated all through the night.

By February things were worse still. Melanie was desperate to get her business back on track but it was clear she was unable to work. She would attend a meeting with her business partner then come home and say she didn't remember a thing. I was angry that her business partner said she just had depression and should pull herself together.

Chapter Four

It was now March and this had been going on for more than 6 months. I had become convinced that my body was now shutting down along with my mind and on several occasions I screamed for Richard or my parents to call for an ambulance as I was 'dying.' Riannon turned 11 in March and the night before her birthday I tried to decorate her cake, something I had always done, every year without difficulty. I just could not do it. I remember smearing the icing all over the cake with my hands. It was ruined. I was so tired and frustrated.

I could not go out without having panic attacks. One time I went food shopping with my Mum and was convinced everyone was looking at me and could tell I was mentally ill. I would look around me and make assumptions about people that they were crazy and that I would end up just like them. I would relate things that were happening on TV to me. Watching the bad X-Factor auditions, I would think that people's opinions of them were the same as their opinions of me. Even though I couldn't watch TV

without this happening I would pretend I was watching it for the sake of Riannon and Richard. I would pretend to laugh when they laughed then become paranoid that they knew I wasn't really laughing. This could go on for hours; I hated every second but tried to act normal for their sake.

Richard was relentless in his pursuit to 'cure' me. He told me my whole life was wrong and that my circumstances growing up had led to this. He lectured me on how to be a better Mum and analysed my every thought. He continued to spend evenings and whole days telling me it was 'just depression' and I need to think in this way, think in that way, turn a negative feeling into a positive. In his mission to help me he was making me question everything and my brain felt thick with mulch. He made me do the breathing exercises from my counselling sessions to try to calm me when I got hysterical but they still didn't work. I spent so long looking into myself at a time when I was so vulnerable that I thought I was beyond help.

My Mum's Record Of What Was Happening

Things just continued to decline. I was so scared, I didn't know what else I could do for Melanie; just be there for her. I knew at weekends when she was with Richard that he told her not to tell me how bad she had been, but I knew. As a family we were all very tense, stressed and scared. We all prayed that a miracle would happen and that the latest tablet would be the one to cure her.

When Melanie said she couldn't decorate Riannon's cake on the night before her birthday as her creative skills had gone I remember being very frightened but I told her not to worry, I would buy another cake. How she held it together for the party I don't know but she did. I think we mustn't forget what a strong person she is and although she was falling apart she managed to make her daughter happy.

Melanie's Dad and I were supposed to be going on holiday three weeks later. I asked Melanie if she would rather we didn't go. She said she was beginning to feel a bit better so we should go. I now know she was lying to us. I asked Richard to stay with her the week we were away.

The last psychiatrist phoned me to say that at their meeting Melanie had said she had thoughts of taking her life and he asked if I felt she would. I said no I didn't but I was shocked she had spoken about it. He said that he too didn't think she would. He said that with her medication she would start to feel less anxious soon and he didn't need to see her for six weeks. Feeling a little reassured by this, we went on holiday. Although still worried we knew Richard was there with her and I phoned every day. She seemed more upbeat on the phone so I felt maybe she was beginning to get a little better slowly. A few days into our holiday when I phoned she seemed very down and I came off the phone feeling worried. But the next day we texted

and she text back saying she was fine with a smiley face.
This reassured me.

Chapter Five

During the last few months I typed the following journal on my computer under the file name 'scared.' I wrote a few lines every few days. This is my collection of memoirs:

I miss my life.

I have convinced myself that I am severely mentally ill and have become incapable of thinking straight.

I have shied away from everything and am now nervous as if I've done something wrong, my feelings are all messed up, I have convinced myself I cannot laugh, am mental and stupid. I have not been relaxing AT all, the only time is when I get a little bit of sleep then it happens all over again. I feel watched and self-conscious even when on my own. I just cannot shake or overcome the strong emotions and feelings which prevent me from believing I'm a good person, in fact, relentlessly tell me otherwise.

I try to 'ignore' – wont go away

I try to distract – only works for a bit

I simply cannot even close my eyes without my memory fading and I am completely locked back in to this nightmare.

I am so afraid that something awful will happen, every second of every day, I cannot see how to get out of this. I'm exhausted. My brain won't work properly. My memory has gone and I feel like a retard. I cannot sleep, my head pounds, it's like a thick fog in my brain, I cannot remember anything good.

I'm ashamed, gutted, confused, and scared out my mind of what the future holds – am so afraid of my own thoughts.

I'm afraid to think, watch TV, read for fear another thought gets implanted in my head and cannot relax for the goddamn life of me. Cannot sleep. Every minute is like a lifetime.

Not sure why this is happening to me but it's made me a nervous wreck and I can't live like this any longer. I fear saying how bad it is to the professionals in case I end up locked up or people say I'm mad which will cause embarrassment to my family, my daughter.

I try so hard every day but my fears are so magnified and my brain so dull I simply cannot do the simplest thing.

It's made me so miserable, I cannot put into words.

My brain is so confused. Feels like time is running out, I cannot have one more bad night, which are so bizarre, I just keep thinking I'm going to die or am going crazy. I cannot sleep, am crippled by this. I'm hot then cold, cannot concentrate on work.

The only escape I have is the few hours sleep I have

got in recent weeks. I've hardly slept in months, I am breathless, my heart paces and I have an explosion in my head that won't go away.

I have now come to the end, I wanted to carry on for my family and for me but I'm not me any more. I cannot walk properly or do anything without getting exhausted. I now feel petrified of going into a mental hospital but do not want my family to be embarrassed. I do not want to end up in a mental hospital and it's gone too far now. I cannot work, I cannot speak, I'm thinking about what to think. My emotions are now numb and feel like I'm going to pass out. Every day I feel like this and it gets harder to do anything each day.

My instincts have gone, my colours and thoughts have gone, I try and try and try to focus on positives but I cannot think straight.

I cannot care for Ri any more, let alone myself. Getting out of the bath is exhausting.

I'm exhausted from the severe lack of sleep and sleeping problems, have strong 'suicidal' / 'sinking to my stomach' feelings that I get at the drop of a hat, and have incredible nerves.

Cannot remember anything, or know the day of the week. My mind tells me I am miserable and cannot smile all through the day and night.

Riannon's Record Of What Happened Over Those Seven Months

Over seven months I literally watched my Mum change in front of my eyes... She started off by being as happy as life could be... Then moments later she would turn into the complete opposite. It was like she had an angel on one shoulder and a devil on the other.

After a few months of being like that there was a big downfall it was like the devil defeated the angel... She just turned into someone who couldn't think... You could tell she couldn't think because her eyes would always look confused if you said anything and it would always take a while for her to understand anything that you would say. I never knew why she was like this, I just thought it was a phase but it went on for far too long. I was so worried and frustrated rolled into one why she was being like this. I didn't like the person she turned into... Someone who couldn't walk up the stairs or even do the simplest things like making a sandwich.

At that time I never really understood what was happening, I did a lot for myself, the rest either my Nan or Richard did. Most of the time my Mum would be very frail and extremely weak, Richard did most things for her to let her relax; I remember one night my Mum grabbed herself by the scruff of the neck and threatened to kill herself right there at that moment. Life was hard but I never thought it would end up the way it did.

Chapter Six

"You can make an omelette," I told myself through gritted teeth. I hardly recognised the person looking back at me in the bedroom mirror. I hadn't smiled in months, my cheeks were sunken and I looked a mess.

"You....Can....Make.....An....Omelette," I repeated slowly, "Now focus. You can, you can!"

I was on my 3rd attempt of making an omelette. I had cooked it dozens of times before, maybe hundreds. I hadn't cooked in a while so today I thought I would. Each day I was documenting my small achievements to try to train my brain to focus on the positives. Every small thing I did got written down, whether cleaning the bathroom or washing up some plates. I had learned this from my counselling sessions and I'd become obsessed with writing down my positives and sticking my favourites up on the wall. It didn't actually make any difference but I figured I had nothing to lose by doing it.

I had become so incompetent, taking hours to complete tasks that I could previously do while standing on my head successfully juggling jelly and hanging upside down. It was unbearable. And here I was trying to cook a stupid omelette and failing spectacularly. I just could not think how to do it. Looking in the mirror one last time I said determinedly "for God's sake, you can do this!" As I left the room and headed back to the kitchen I felt a strange sense of something very disturbing happening. I returned to the stove. Frying pan in hand, eggs in pan, I felt my brain finally, after months of decaying, slip out of my head and onto the kitchen floor. I was mortified! In that moment I felt like my brain had disappeared. If you had asked me what my name was I would have stared at you blankly.

Terrified, I now felt like my legs weren't working and I limped around my flat, petrified. "This can't be happening!" I phoned Richard. "My brain's gone, my brain's gone, I'm dying!" I screamed. "Please, please call the Crisis Line!" Richard pleaded. We had been given this number in case of emergencies by the last psychiatrist. I was so frightened. What if they locked me up? "I'll be back as soon as I can" Richard said. "Now I want you to call that number, do you hear?!"

Shaking, I put the phone down and dialled the number scrawled on the note paper that was by the phone. "Hello?" Someone answered. "Can I help you?" the kind sounding lady asked gently down the phone. I couldn't think. I put the phone down. Minutes later she called back.

"What's your name?" She asked.

"Melanie," I replied.

"OK Melanie, talk to me. You've made the first step by contacting us."

"My….my…..my brain has slipped out my head." I was aware this sounded ridiculous.

"Do you feel as if you can't cope?" she asked.

"Yes," I said. "I can't cope."

"Do you feel like harming yourself?"

"Yes."

"OK. Well you need to go to your nearest Accident and Emergency hospital."

"OK" I said. I put the phone down. Go to A & E?

As I paced around the flat climbing the walls I thought about killing myself right then and there. Riannon was in her room. It was getting late. I grabbed a bottle of wine from the fridge and my sleeping pills. With that, Richard opened the front door. He took one look at me and shook his head. "Lets get you to mine," he said. He scooped me up, threw some things in a bag and drove me and Riannon to his. Another sleepless night ensued and we all went to a shopping centre the next day. I tried to get through the day the best I could and we all returned to Richards. I remember we had bought Riannon some new shoes but I don't remember much else about that day. Richard and Riannon went out on an impromptu trip to Tesco at about 8pm and I found myself in the kitchen, pills in one hand, wine bottle in another.

Nothing different to any other day happened to make me pick that moment to die. I just simply could not go on any more. As fate would have it there were road blocks meaning Richard and Riannon were gone for two hours. I deliberated for that entire time whether to do it or not. I took a handful but spat them out. My heart was pounding. I could see my reflection in the kitchen window by the sink. I was watching myself while my life hung in the balance. What was I doing? This was crazy. I was crazy. I was desperate. I had reached the end. Do I? Don't I? I had taken all the pills out their boxes. There were loads. I picked them up and put them all in my mouth then swigged a mouthful of wine. I held them in my mouth. I put all the packets back neatly so Richard and Riannon would not know what I have done. I headed upstairs and went to bed. I still hadn't swallowed. Do I? Don't I? I heard the front door. They were back. I swallowed. I imagined I would fall into a deep sleep and not wake up. I closed my eyes and waited for peace.

I suddenly realised I had not even written Riannon a goodbye note! So I sat up, switched the lamp on and scribbled on the back of a piece of paper on the bedside table telling her how much I loved her and how none of this was her fault. I felt so relieved that I had thought to do that and I switched off the lamp and drifted off to sleep.

> Ri, I love you my darling with all my heart. You will be a beautiful woman, keep your attitude girl, keep your spirit, keep strong; this will seem impossible for you but I know that you will be ok.

Riannon's Record Of What Happened That Day

It was 2 or 3 days before the half term ended... That day me, my Mum and Richard went to the shopping centre... That day my Mum was very nervous and also very stroppy... Most of the time she was very out of it and was like she was in her own world, overall it was a nice time shopping.

That night; I was doing some homework with Richard, the time was around 8.00... we ran out of pens and we decided to go to Tesco, we called up to Mum who was up the stairs in bed but not sleeping – she decided to stay there… So me and Richard hopped into the car not suspecting anything and drove away in the darkness leaving my Mum in the house alone…

We returned maybe one or two hours later (due to road blocks)… we called up to Mum but she seemed to be sleeping, we finished my homework with the new pens and then shortly went up (probably around 10 or 11) Richard was reading me a story and we heard a weird sound that came from the hallway… 'MMM' and then a loud stumble… Richard gently said 'wait there.'

Of course I stuck my head out to see what was happening and there standing there in front of my very eyes was my Mum standing there with white all around her mouth making the same groany sound… Her dark chocolate eyes looked half dead as they twitched along with the rest of her face… She tried to speak but all that came out were horrible sounds that I still remember today, the image I saw was just horrific… Richard kept asking questions like 'Mel what have you done, whats happening?' And the only response he got was 'TABLETS' In an out of breath tone, Richard's face drained as he tried to act strong but inside he was dying; just like I thought my Mum was! Whilst Richard was asking all these questions he was resting my Mum on the bed and on the phone to the ambulance.

A few moments later the doorbell rang and the most complicated door I ever saw in my life stood before me *locked in all types of different ways... I was scared I would take too long to open the door and it would be too late... she would be dead.*

Somehow I opened the door and the ambulance crew rushed upstairs and took my Mum away as a young nurse was calming me and reassuring me it was going to be alright... I had no idea what was going on as my face froze with icy tears rolling down my cheeks, as the ambulance took my Mum away me and Richard followed straight to the hospital.

When we arrived Richard tried many times to call my Nan and granddad who were unfortunately on holiday... Richard was leaving them many voice messages, text messages, emails any way to get hold of them he tried... I remember falling asleep on his lap with tears still rolling down my face. Maybe around the time of 2 or 3 in the morning they let me see my Mum... they led us both into a curtain closed room with my Mum laying there with tubes surrounding her. I watched Richard wipe away a tear as he stared at my Mum who was fighting for her life.

She then got moved to another part of the hospital. I remember waking up on the floor with coats all around me, and seeing my auntie rushing in and taking me to Burger King and she tried to change the subject.

Melanie Burnell

Chapter Seven

I remember waking up in hospital surrounded by tubes. Riannon was asleep on some coats on the floor next to me. My first thought was 'Shit it didn't work.' My mind raced with ways to get out of here. I realised now more than ever just how much I wanted to die. I had been trying to resist my suicidal thoughts for so long; I had tried to fight the will to die. But now, today, I realised just how much I wanted this nightmare to end.

Some time later a psychiatrist came to see me. "You took a massive overdose" he said in a serious tone. "How do you feel that it didn't work?"

"Relieved," I lied forcing a smile.

"Hmmm," he said.

"When can I go home?" I asked.

"Not until we can ascertain why you did it" he said. "We'll speak later." He left. I tried to tie one of the tubes I was hooked up to around my neck but nothing happened. The thought of jumping in front of a train would not leave my mind. I was fixated with wanting to kill myself.

I noticed there was a long orange chord in the toilet cubicle and a chair below it. I planned to hang myself from it when the nurses were not watching me so closely. My sister, Richard and Riannon came to see me but I don't remember much. My sister later told me that I was crawling around on the floor saying that my legs didn't work. I vaguely remember a nurse telling me to stop acting like this in front of my daughter.

I took my chance when I thought no one was watching. I locked myself in the cubicle, climbed on the chair and tied the thin chord around my neck. I've no doubt now that it would have snapped once I'd jumped but it never got to that stage because Richard kicked the door down and came rushing in with the nurses who cut me free.

They sat me in front of the psychiatrist. "Why did you try to kill yourself?" he asked. I didn't know what to say. I wracked my brains.

"I'm fine now" I said. "I just want to go home."

"We can't let you go home unless we are certain you won't try to kill yourself again." They told me they would be admitting me to the Acute Assessment Centre for psychological assessment. I was scared.

My Mum's Record Of What Was Happening

Saturday 31st March was a very hot day in Majorca and that evening we went out to dinner with friends, we'd had a lovely evening. Unbeknown to us the most terrible event was about to happen back home. We went to bed and both our phones were turned off. Sunday 1st April we woke up and did our packing as we were flying home that evening. It was lunch time before we realised our phones were not on. I put my phone on and more messages than I could count came through saying Melanie was in hospital. I remember my whole body shaking with fear. I tried to call Richard but there was no reply; I tried to phone Riannon – no reply. I tried to call my other daughter Caroline – no reply. I tried to call Stuart, Caroline's partner – he put the phone down after a couple of rings so I kept calling him until he picked up. I spoke with Caroline and begged her to find out what happened and call me back. Time I remember just seemed to stand still. Caroline called back and said she had spoken with Melanie, she had taken an overdose but the relief she was alive was overwhelming.

By now I had also spoken to Richard and he said I needed to call the hospital to speak to the nurse to make sure Riannon will be picked up by a member of the family otherwise she would be taken into care. I was so scared for Riannon. I called the hospital, called Caroline and made arrangements for Caroline to collect Riannon then meet us at the airport then we would take charge of Riannon. The journey home to England is just a blur. I only remember seeing Riannon and Caroline and being relieved to be back home – not knowing what was about to unfold.

Social Services called a couple of hours after returning

home to check I had Riannon. Richard called to say Melanie was being transferred to an assessment centre as we speak. I called them and I was able to speak with Melanie which was reassuring. They told us to come into the centre in the morning to speak with the psychiatrist. Social services phoned and explained that if Melanie was to attempt her life again she would not get Riannon back.

Riannon's Record Of What Happened That Day

I remember that I was meant to be getting my side fringe cut into a full fringe; my Mum then got moved to where I visited her before I got my fringe cut… it was very scary, me, my nan and granddad went into her room and I couldn't imagine my Mum living in there it was just so confusing how just a few days ago we were on the sofa together and now she was in here and I was at Nans. We got told to go outside because it was no place for children, after maybe an hour we went to get my hair done, then me and my granddad went back to say hi and show Mum my new hair.

My Mum's Record Of What Happened That Day

We went to the Assessment Centre. I hugged Melanie. She looked so frail and so ill. She was genuinely pleased to see us. We spoke with a psychiatrist who was trying to work out what had made her do what she did. I told him what she had just said to me – that she was scared she had become like a vegetable and was no longer any use to her daughter or her family. They questioned if she was bi-polar. They too were baffled. They needed more time to assess her. I was so upset seeing my daughter in this state and in a psychiatric unit. I was scared of the term 'Mental Illness' and didn't want to admit my daughter was a patient in a psychiatric hospital. I wanted to take her home but I knew I would not be able to give her the help she so needed. It was then that I felt relieved that something would be done finally.

Melanie Burnell

Chapter Eight

When I arrived at the Assessment centre I met a girl called Jo. She too had tried to kill herself the same night as me. She was ten years older than me and was a recovering alcoholic. She had tried to electrocute herself in the bath while holding an iron. We stayed together for the next three days, talking about our thoughts and fears. Sitting on the bench outside in the fenced off courtyard she said, "Do you know how difficult it is to kill yourself?" I shook my head. "I've tried many times" she said matter-of-factly and proceeded to tell me all the ways she had tried and failed to end her life over the years.

"What about jumping out of a building?" I said.

She paused. "I haven't tried that" she said and we both laughed.

My time in here was a bit of a daze. I remember the kitchen cupboards and drawers were all locked and they took my belt and shoe laces off me. After three days, Jo was discharged home and I was told that I would be transferred to a secure psychiatric hospital. My worst fear

had come true; I was going to be locked up and I couldn't stop screaming.

My Mum's Record Of What Happened That Day

That afternoon I had popped to the supermarket. When I got home there was a message on my answer phone. It was a desperate Melanie saying there were taking her away and she would never see us again. She was crying and saying to tell Riannon that she loved her. As I listened to the message, I too cried and cried for some time after. When I could gather my thoughts I rang the Assessment Centre and they explained that Melanie was being taken to a long stay hospital as they felt she would benefit from being an in-patient as she was quite ill.

That evening we went to the hospital. It was a very scary place. We had to be buzzed in two doors, walk across a courtyard and be buzzed in another door. Melanie was very disturbed at being here and frightened. I cuddled her and remember telling her she would be home soon – I believed this.

Chapter Nine

I remember being absolutely terrified as I walked in. Floor to ceiling glass separated the patients from the staff. I was locked up with some 30 or so people with varying levels of mental illnesses. It was all I'd envisaged and worse. It was a really scary place. I'd barely managed to settle in when, a day after my admission, Jo turned up, as a patient, covered in bruises.

"Oh my God, what happened?" I asked.

"Jumped out of a building" she said.

For the first couple of weeks I was placed on suicide watch where a member of staff stayed by my side at all times. All I could think about was killing myself. As with the last place all my belts and laces had been taken off me but it didn't stop me searching out ways to hang myself with the tiniest of chords I had found on a pair of my size 6 jogging bottoms. My room had white walls and a frosted out window. There was the main area where there was a pool table and two huge tables and the heaviest chairs imaginable. Mostly we would just sit here being watched

and monitored by the staff who took lots of notes from behind the glass. We would also eat our food here. There was a communal TV room with a couple of private visiting areas. There were different wings to the hospital which you needed a special security card pass to enter depending on the section your room was in. At some point someone had thoughtfully attached mine to my wrist with an elastic band although I had no recollection of this happening. Some of the patients kept losing their passes and I would often see someone behind the glass inset of the heavy fire doors that led in to the main area, banging to be let through. I'd alert one of the nurses and they would buzz them through. However, this happened so regularly and I seemed to be the only person letting staff know that eventually I too turned a blind eye and patients would be banging in vein behind the doors for ages!

My room was by the entrance and I could hear new people being admitted at night. New people were admitted regularly. Some people just stayed for a few days, others had been there for many months. A lot of the people who were admitted had tried to kill themselves and many had bandaged wrists. We were all on a cocktail of strong drugs which were administered three times a day. In their West-Indian accents the nurses would shout: "MEDICATION!!" and we'd have to queue up at the medicine hatch and they would dish out the pills checked off against a chart, in little white cups. I was on more than 10 pills a day. They called these strong combinations 'Treatment' doses. They had some horrendous side effects and it crossed my mind not to take them. They said it was a case of finding the right ones but along the way the side effects included being really spaced out, feeling like my body was going rigid and one concoction even made my tongue swell up and go stiff – that was a terrifying experience and I had to take a special antidote to counteract the effects. The drugs made some people pass out and others were very sick. We were all closely monitored. We had regular blood tests and were weighed and had our blood pressure taken daily. I became convinced that it was a government drug testing unit and would send my Mum and sister garbled voice messages saying they needed to get me out of there and that no one got out, they were kept in a room underground!

Ten days after my admission we had a 'Patient's Meeting.' These took place on a Sunday and were very strange indeed; quite ridiculous. All 30 or so very drugged up, mentally ill patients would sit round the table and discuss their hospital issues with two or three members of staff, while one of us took minutes. The issues ranged from requesting smooth not crunchy peanut butter at teatime to "The guy sharing my room stinks, make him shower!" During this meeting I stood up and screamed, "We've got to get out of here! They are testing drugs on us!" Everything seemed as though I was watching a video tape that was stuck, the people in the room appeared to be on 'play' then 'stop', 'rewind' then 'play' again. Two members of staff grabbed me and marched me to my room and threw me on my bed. I felt like my brain was on melt down. I remember laying on my bed and thinking my mind had been warped and that we were all being poisoned by the food and drugs.

The staff members who were looking after me later told my Mum that I just stared at them blankly and took around 10 minutes to 'come round.' When they left my room I grabbed a bottle of hairspray from the side (which shouldn't have been allowed in my room, all sprays were locked away) and sprayed it into my mouth. I hoped it would kill me, saving me from my fate of being drug tested on.

When my Mum, sister and Richard came to visit me that evening, something really terrifying happened. Have you ever died in a dream? The experience feels very real and it is only after you wake up that you realise you are still alive. Well I had an awake experience of that and I can honestly say it was the most terrifying hours of my life.

My Mum's Record Of What Happened That Day

Myself, Melanie's sister and Richard went to the hospital at visiting time and found Melanie in a worse state than she had previously been. We were in one of the family rooms and she was very aggressive and agitated. The nurse told us Melanie had to be removed from the weekly Patient's Meeting that morning as she was shouting that this was a 'government conspiracy' and that 'nobody ever gets out of here.' She was clearly in a very disturbed state and I sensed we should call for help. I could see the veins on her head bulging and her fingers went rigid and bent upwards. The look on her face will never leave me; her face was contorted and she appeared to want to attack me.

We hit the emergency buzzer and Melanie was led into the treatment room kicking and screaming. They tried giving her a sedative but she refused to take it and was screaming out. Myself and her sister were told to leave the room while Richard and 4 nurses tried to calm her down. Standing outside the room we heard her animal like howls. The whole situation was so difficult to listen to. Not knowing what was happening to her was very scary. A nurse came out to say he would call the emergency doctor to see her. Melanie's screams continued.

Melanie Burnell

Chapter Ten

I was petrified. I thought that my arms and legs no longer worked, that I was just a 'head on a stick' – a vegetable, unable to move and that I was dying. Richard was in the room with all the nurses and doctors. They were trying to hold me down and Richard was begging me to trust him and stop fighting them all. "You're killing me!" I screamed. I believed he was. I believed they all were. For almost three hours the nurses and doctors tried to sedate me. I'd stop struggling for a bit then get another surge of energy. I felt I was fighting for my life. I vigorously flapped my arms and legs to show Richard that my limbs were redundant. The belief that I was paralysed was so strong that at some stage during the ordeal I decided it was better to die than to live a life where I could not use my arms and legs. I had visions of being trapped in a body that wouldn't work, being unable to communicate and ridiculed. I imagined huge screens beaming live links showing my lifeless body around the world. I thought the nurses were taking pictures of me on their phones. I tried to kill myself by holding my breath. I was convinced now that Richard was trying to save me and I was getting more and more angry with him. "Just let me die!" I now screamed as I fought with them all. My strength he said afterwards was astonishing. Eventually the sedation took hold and I laid still. I was exhausted and dripping in sweat. Richard and one of the nurses lead me back to my room.

Richard put me in my bed and, exhausted himself, stroked my hair and face. He stayed there until I fell asleep. I awoke some hours later. One of the nurses, Mos, was sitting beside me on a chair. I got up to go to the toilet. I'll never forget that moment.

"Oh my God!" I said, "I can move my legs!"

"Yes," said Mos. "You can."

I was so happy in that moment.

I had suffered an Acute Psychotic Episode; a complete break from reality. It was an experience I will never forget but at least it meant that the doctors now knew what they were treating – psychosis. The word scared me. Well it sounded like psycho right? Was I a psychopath? The Doctor said that it was now a case of finding the right type of anti-psychotic treatment and with each change of medication my family waited with baited breath. During the next three months of treatment I experienced some very strange things but thankfully I never had another attack like that.

My Mum's Record Of What Happened That Day

I felt relieved that this had happened in hospital as I would never have known how to deal with it. The next day Melanie appeared calmer and we were advised that she was suffering from psychosis – something we had not heard of until now. We were told she would get better with treatment and we were very encouraged by this.

Chapter Eleven

Still believing it was a drugs testing unit, I became convinced that one of the other patients Tammy was trying to communicate with me through winks and nods that this was a massive cover-up, that we were all part of a government testing unit. Tammy never spoke so I don't know how I came to that conclusion! One day I whispered to her, "write everything down!" That evening at dinner she passed me a note. "I now have all the evidence I need", I thought as I opened it. It read simply: 'Sweets, friends, clothes, shopping.'

Life in the hospital was hard. We had to ask for everything. All our toiletries were locked away. If we wanted a shower we had to ask for it to be unlocked then ask for a towel.

The panic alarms went off all day and night as patients got aggressive with each other and staff. A few times a week we would have Relaxation classes with the Occupational Therapists but they weren't very relaxing as you'd hear patients screaming and banging outside the

room. Sometimes we went over to the sports hall to play badminton which I enjoyed. We had art therapy classes which were good as it took my mind off things for a bit. We had coping workshops and did cookery but we were all often so out of it on medication that we didn't really engage that well. There was a strict routine. Breakfast was at 8.00am or 8.30am on the weekends, tea and biscuit break at 11.00am, lunch was at 12.30pm, another tea break at 2.00pm, then visiting at 4.00pm with more tea and biscuits. Dinner was at 6.00pm then 2nd visiting at 7pm, then evening tea and toast at 9.00pm and bed by 11.00pm.

For the first time in a long time I was eating well. The food was nice especially the puddings; cake and custard or donuts with lots of cream. We would all queue up and the menu would be pinned up next to us. Bizarrely the menu very rarely included the items on offer, as if to confuse us. You'd get to the hatch and ask for chicken pasta bake as that caught your eye on the menu, only to be told the choice was beef casserole or tuna pasta!

A lot of the time I just sat silently at the table in my own world, trying desperately not to attract the attention of the other patients. Even Jo was volatile, kicking off and shouting at the staff so I tried to keep myself to myself. I spent a lot of time in my room as I felt most safe there. There was a little courtyard that was locked but was sometimes opened and I liked sitting outside feeling the sun on my face.

My Mum's Record Of What Happened That Day

On Melanie's 31st birthday we took her in cards but not her presents as it seemed inappropriate. I explained she would have her presents when she came out. I felt so sad but as always tried to remain upbeat for her sake. Melanie was like a zombie, clearly from the medication. She was now not speaking. I was getting lots of texts saying she knows this is a government conspiracy and she will die in here and that she loved us. Clearly her paranoia was getting worse. Her medication was changed with yet again our hopes dashed of a quick recovery. This new drug although appearing to make Melanie more settled again gave her very high blood pressure and now she was also on blood pressure tablets.

She had good days and bad days; good days she would speak and bad days she just looked around her like a frightened kitten and never spoke a word. As a mother I became so concerned for her and would call the hospital often. She would call me and tell me something wasn't right and when I called the hospital to tell them what she had just said to me they said they could see her in front of them looking happy and laughing. I knew she was paranoid as that was part of her illness, but I still believed what she told me. Every time I visited I asked for her dirty washing. She was unable to distinguish between what was dirty and what was clean. She also no longer cared about her personal hygiene.

Melanie Burnell

Chapter Twelve

Night times were hard to get used to. The staff used to patrol the ward and you could hear their keys jangling as they walked past. It felt just how I imagined prison to be like. And then, bizarrely, every hour they would switch your light on and off! Then in the morning they would ask, "How did you sleep?"

"Not very f*****g well! You kept switching my light on!" They would do this to 'check' on us. Patients would be screaming which, together with the light switching and plastic pillow and mattress didn't make sleeping any easier than before I got admitted to hospital. I really hated being there. It never crossed my mind that I was ill and would get better.

I continued to take the strong sleeping pills they offered and gradually got used to my new surroundings sleeping a little more each night. I asked them to stop with the lights and they said I could leave my wall light on instead and they would be able to check on me without switching the main light on. The wall light was bright so I

covered it with an orange T-Shirt attached with an elastic band and I'd drift off to sleep in the warm orange glow. Without even realising it, I stopped wanting to die and started sleeping again. Night times became my sanctuary.

After a few weeks the strong and persistent desire to kill myself had slowly melted away and I was allowed out for 2 hours leave each day. When I saw my Mum behind the glass door signing in at reception I would imagine them telling her I was not well enough to come out today and then take me off somewhere else where I would never see them again. I would get really anxious as I couldn't communicate behind the sound proof glass. I would be so relieved when the doors opened and I could leave with my Mum.

My Mum's Record Of What Happened

Melanie's leave turned into a nightmare. I would pick her up and she would immediately start saying she had 'a plan' that I must help her with so that she wouldn't have to go back. I spent the whole two hours of leave trying to get her in the right frame of mind for our journey back. Although I loved to see her I wished she hadn't been given leave as I found it hard to cope with her.

Riannon's Record Of What Happened

I never liked visiting Mum even though it was the only time I got to see her before she got leave, it was hard to get into the building because of all the locks and security and when we finally got in we had to sign a book with what times and stuff then we had to go through where all the other patients were; then into a small room where my Mum would sit almost like she didn't want to be there but inside I knew she did. One time I remember when we said good bye she mouthed 'I will never see you again.' As tears filled up my eyes I decided to ignore it let it pass but inside I was wondering it might be true…

Melanie Burnell

Chapter Thirteen

I looked forward to seeing my family every day at visiting time although I often said nothing, spaced out on medication. Riannon came occasionally which was lovely and we made each other little presents. She would write me stories and make me pictures which I would put up in my room and I would make her little decorated trinkets and silk paintings that I made in Art Therapy classes. As time went on I was allowed out for longer leave and I'd read Riannon a story in bed at my Mums which I loved. She always cried when I had to go back.

Every Tuesday was Ward Round where all the patients would individually get assessed by the Doctor and Psychiatrist on progress that week. You would have a medication review and they would look at all the notes that the nurses had made on you. Those who were deemed well enough to go home were discharged. At every Ward Round I hoped and prayed they would let me out, but it didn't happen and I knew I was condemned to yet another week's incarceration. At each of my meetings there would

be the Doctor, Psychiatrist, one of the nurses, one of the Occupational Therapists, my Mum and me.

Each time they asked how I was feeling and I'd tell them "I feel OK now, please let me go home." But each time they would say "not yet." The next best thing was being granted leave. If I was not allowed leave due to not doing so well I would get really upset. Over the weeks and months I watched other patients who had been admitted at a similar time to me, be discharged and I wondered if I'd ever get out. I felt institutionalised and worried I would never live a normal life again.

My Mum's Record Of What Happened

At her next Ward Round the Doctor announced that Melanie must come off the current medication as it was unsafe due to her high blood pressure. They were to put her on a treatment dose of the medication she had been on when she tried to take her life. This agitated Melanie as she knew this was not a medication that agreed with her. Still the Doctors said she must go on it. It was about this time that it was being decided what care would be appropriate for Melanie when she was discharged from hospital. Initially it was decided she would be assigned a Social Worker. Then it was decided that the Early Intervention Team should come in to visit Melanie to decide if they would be better suited to her needs. We were told that it would be a good thing if they accepted her. We had our fingers crossed and the news was good; Beatrice was to be Melanie's Care Worker. As soon as Melanie was introduced to her she liked her and so did I. I knew we had the best possible care in place upon Melanie's discharge. We just had to get the medication right.

Melanie Burnell

Chapter Fourteen

I was very quiet and withdrawn in hospital. Staff even affectionately referred to me as a 'worrier' and I had to learn to manage my panic attacks. I was allowed two little blue pills, on top of my other meds when I started panicking which really helped to calm me down. Once I began having leave, they used it to bargain with me. They started saying that if I had the pills I would not be allowed on leave, so I had to learn to overcome them on my own as I didn't want to miss out on my leave. It was a far cry from my real personality; my zesty, feisty personality seemed a distant memory. One day one of the nurses asked me if I'd always been 'a bit of a worrier.' Thinking it might help to get me out quicker I said yes, hoping that they might think I had always been quiet and that it was not a reflection of my illness. When my Mum found out I'd lied she went mad! "Melanie's one of the loudest, most confident people you could wish to meet!" she announced, putting the nurse straight at visiting time and rolling her eyes in annoyance at me.

One night I woke up disorientated after a bad dream where I was dying and looked at my watch. It said 5.00. I was really confused, not sure if it was 5.00 in the morning or 5.00 at night. I walked down the long corridor to the office.

"Is it morning or night?" I asked the nurse.

"It's morning now go back to bed, you have no clothes on!" she said.

As a heavy smoker of almost 20 years I was surprised at how easily I adapted to not being able to smoke in there. I think I was that ill that I just accepted it and I can honestly say I never once craved a cigarette in there or since I've been out! For other patients however it was really difficult not being able to smoke and people were always kicking off about it. One girl, Marie, used to walk around with three nicorette inhalers in her mouth at once! Group walks were fun, someone always tried to bolt. I thought about making a run for it myself but realised I didn't know the area.

One of the strangest things that happened to me was when I started speaking in a strong West-Indian accent! Many of the nurses were of West-Indian origin and for some reason I began involuntarily talking like them! My Mum was really upset and asked me to stop it but I really couldn't. It stopped as suddenly as it started after a week or so and now I can't do the accent even if I try! My favourite time was tea, toast and bed. At tea time I would have a hot chocolate and slice of toast slathered with peanut butter then have my evening meds then take myself off to bed. Life in the hospital did feel like being in prison and patients who had also been in prison said it was worse. "At least you get TV's in your own room in prison," they said.

We had our tea and coffee out of plastic cups but the plates were ceramic. One of the other patients launched one at me one dinner time and it just missed my head! The staff were a mixed bag; some were really lovely and caring, others were not. Most were West Indian and they all talked about God a lot. There were some characters in there, that's for sure. Tommy would shuffle around looking at the floor declaring "I have a poem, can I read it to anyone?" Mo would stand with his trousers around his ankles and his fingers in his ears shouting "LOCO-LOCO-LOCO-LOCO!" and would spit at people. Pete was obsessively in love with Alisha Dixon and would not stop talking about her especially when she came on the TV. He honestly believed they would end up together. Rob would run around screaming "my dick won't work!" Deborah ran around naked on several occasions. Elizabeth always wore gloves. Annie put so many things down her bra; she would store her electronic cigarette, face powder, security tag and a host of other things including her favourite sweets. As I got better I found her really funny and she used to have me in stitches. She had the room next to me and would often come in my room until one of the staff kicked her out.

My Mum's Record Of What Happened

The weeks were passing by, it was now May. We were at Ward Round when as usual Melanie said she felt fit to be discharged and as usual the professionals disagreed. But her leave, which had been cancelled the previous week, was reinstated. In fact she was told she could have 'weekend leave' on Friday if she remained OK the rest of the week. I felt this was not a good thing as Melanie had certainly been agitated this last week on the new medication. I voiced this to the Doctor but he said he felt she would be fine.

I picked her up on the Friday and collected her medication for the weekend. We came home and had lunch with Richard. Melanie and Richard then went back to Melanie's flat. On arriving there she was screaming and shouting at Richard to get out of her flat saying she didn't want him there. He managed to calm her but clearly she was not well enough to be home yet. Richard said she had a disturbed nights sleep. The next day they decided to go for a walk on the Downs, a scenic place near by. Once in the car Melanie changed her mind and said she wanted to go home. Once home she said she wanted to go to the downs. She changed her mind 4 more times! That evening Melanie, Richard, myself, her dad and Riannon went for a meal. Melanie didn't speak a word all evening. Where was our Melanie and would she ever come back? We were totally exhausted and all hope was vanishing.

The next day she was becoming very agitated and

aggressive. I knew I needed to get her back to hospital. Me and Richard tried to get her into the car but she went rigid and refused to get in. We were about to call an ambulance when she finally got in. I rang ahead to the hospital so they were expecting us. I was so relieved to have her back in hospital!

On Tuesday's Ward Round once again Melanie was asking for discharge and once again was declined, together with being told her leave had once again been cancelled. Also she was told she was to come off her medication as it was clearly making her very anxious. This time she was given a drug called Olanzapine. We were told this was the final drug they were able to prescribe so we knew everything hinged on it working. We felt so desperate we just couldn't allow ourselves to think of the consequences if this drug didn't work. Melanie was told this drug would make her put on weight so she had to think about what she ate being especially careful of sweet things.

After a few days Melanie seemed calmer but was always desperate for chocolate – a snickers bar or two! It was hard to deny her the pleasure of a bar of chocolate. The Doctor said he was confident this medication was working and reinstated her hours leave. Melanie was so pleased. She was given 4 hours leave at the weekend. We could see she was getting a lot better but was already starting to put on weight.

Melanie Burnell

.

Chapter Fifteen

On my fourth drug concoction something amazing happened. I felt like a light switch had been turned on. I could feel my colours were coming back and my senses were returning. However, I was still just as confused over 'The Sticker System.' Behind the glassed office was a large white board with every patient's written name on it along with short-hand notes documenting things like if a patient was on leave, blood pressure results and coloured stickers. There were red, yellow, green and blue stickers assigned to each name and these could change from day to day; one day you might be blue, one day you might be red. The theories on what these stickers meant varied from patient to patient but the most popular one was that they were related to when you were allowed home. And since none of us wanted to be there it became quite a fixation for many of us.

"Oh my God, you're on a blue, you're going to be going home soon!"

"Oh, you've been put on a red, that means you're to

75

be checked every 15 minutes and won't be going home for at least another month!" I have since found out the stickers relate to the after care team you are assigned to!

There was also a funny hierarchy system. If you were 'voluntary' as opposed to 'sectioned' you were seen by fellow patients as somehow less ill and could leave any time you wanted. There was a real 'them and us' divide but in reality none of us could leave when we wanted because we would simply become sectioned and being 'voluntary' really meant that you were told, as I was, "unless you come voluntarily, we will section you." The days were very long with not much to do. Playing cards was always good to pass the time. It was funny though because each of us was playing our own rules and I'm sure that to anyone looking in it would have seemed ridiculous! But it kept us entertained; me and Annie would play for hours. I would always win but really I don't think either of us had a clue what we were doing! I knew I was getting better when my sense of humour returned. I counted all the cards one day and realised we were short by seven. So the people who were 'a few cards short of a deck' were actually playing with a few cards short of the deck! No one else found this funny but I couldn't stop laughing.

My Mum's Record Of What Happened

By the next Ward Round Melanie was so excited at the prospect of being discharged. She asked the Doctor what she always asked her each week, "when can I go home?" He said "Now!" In fact she had one week's leave only having to return for the final ward round next Tuesday! At last, Melanie was finally on the road to recovery.

Riannon's Record Of What Happened

A couple of months passed and Mum's leave increased and her weekends away got more frequent and before we knew she was back, to this day I still remember her face as it twitched and I still remember those three months like it was yesterday but everything happens for a reason and I feel like its made, me, my nan, my granddad, my auntie and of course my Mum stronger.

Melanie Burnell

Chapter Sixteen

After three long months I was eventually discharged. I was so happy. As I said Goodbye to all the staff and patients, bags packed, with a huge smile on my face, one of the new girls with bandaged wrists and sunken eyes looked at me.

"You're so lucky" she said, "I'm never going to get out of here."

"Oh you will," I assured her.

As I left she shouted after me "but I'm on a green sticker!"

Melanie Burnell

Chapter Seventeen

I caught Judith's steely gaze as I entered the cold cramped room. She smiled at me smugly. Judith, my business partner had called a meeting with our accountant a few days after I was released from hospital. The accountant was a long standing associate of hers from years before we went into partnership and I had always felt she was Judith's friend over and above being our accountant. I felt very uncomfortable as I sat down on the hard chair. My Mum sat down next to me. I'd had a funny feeling about the meeting and had asked her to come along for support.

"The business is not profitable," said the accountant to me firmly. "The website needs to be closed down."

I was devastated. After all I'd been through I couldn't bear the thought that it was all for nothing. I looked at her stern face. It was the first time I had met her as Judith used to deal with her alone. I decided I didn't like her.

"But I've put so much into it," I said. "Surely we can give it another chance?"

"I'm afraid not" she said. "Now you have to walk away, sign the site over fully to Judith so that she can close it down."

"No" I said. I looked at my Mum in disbelief.

"Why can't they give it another go?" my Mum asked.

"Because the business has debts" she said. She turned to me. "Unless you have £20k to put into it you'll have to walk away."

I felt completely trapped. What could I do? Judith looked at me but said nothing. The accountant handed me a sheet of paper to sign. With tears in my eyes I signed my name.

Chapter Eighteen

I moved into my Mums when I was first released from hospital and before I knew it I was back at home with Riannon. At first I thought about my time in hospital every day; I used humour to cope with that, after all I'd just come out of a psychiatric hospital. There were only two responses to that – laugh or cry!

I went out and bought new bits and pieces to decorate my flat like brightly coloured cushions, fresh new bedding and pink cupcake themed accessories for my kitchen. I felt like I'd been given a second lease of life and my colours had come back stronger than ever. I wanted to reflect my new happy state of mind in my surroundings.

Before long I was back driving again and I felt I'd regained my independence. I had come such a long way from feeling institutionalised just a few weeks before.

My Mum's Record Of What Happened

Once Melanie was discharged from hospital I found it very hard to 'let go.' I was constantly concerned if I didn't call her several times a day to check how she was. In fact Melanie was amazing and quickly reintegrated back into everyday life. I felt so grateful for the help she received in hospital even though it was a very traumatic time. I never thought I would get my daughter back.

Chapter Nineteen

I found adjusting to life with Richard very difficult. His intense, over bearing persona and miserable outlook were bringing me down and I felt like I needed to break away from him. His mean and moody demeanour, which I'd found so attractive at the beginning of our relationship, was now grating on me. The more I got back to my 'old self' – someone he had never really known – the more I realised we were not a good match. Psychosis had changed me – albeit temporarily, but I had gone from being vibrant and outgoing to quiet and withdrawn by the time we met. As the 'old me' was returning I realised that the nervous, unconfident woman he fell in love with was no longer there. In her place was a lively, happy and positive person who didn't want her wings clipped. I told him how I felt and how although I appreciated all he had done for me I did not feel we were right for each other. He was upset but accepted it and we went our separate ways.

I felt free.

Gradually over a few months I thought about hospital

less and less until it became a distant memory. My care worker Beatrice, from the Early Intervention Team, came to see me once a week. She kept telling me how well I was doing which was reassuring. She helped to give me the confidence to return to my every day life. "You were so poorly in hospital" she'd say, "just look at you now!" Beatrice explained the importance of relaxing and not over doing things. She didn't want me to relapse – something that could easily happen. Although I felt great I was very vulnerable. The fact that care workers remain in contact with patients for three years after discharge from hospital was a reflection of that.

It was very restful relaxing at home and I took so much pleasure from little comforts like being able to watch TV, make a cup of tea when I fancied and sleeping on a real mattress with crisp fresh cotton sheets. I was looking after myself well, eating properly and taking things easy. Plus I loved being back around Riannon. The spring in her step and the beautiful sweet smell of body spray that followed her from room to room were things I had missed in hospital. She adjusted to everything really well.

At first I was very afraid of becoming ill again. I didn't want to risk my mental health deteriorating so spent my time resting and staying happy, healthy and positive. I made sure I had enough sleep at night and spent quality time with Riannon, my Mum and Dad and friends. I felt somehow stronger as a person for having come through such a horrendous illness and surviving three months in a psychiatric hospital. I felt so grateful that the 'me' I knew had returned – I could think clearly, smile and laugh again. I now laughed harder and longer at things I found funny than I ever had. It was a wonderful feeling.

I was still on anti-psychotic medication although it was a much lower dose than when I was in hospital. Every few weeks my doctor gradually reduced the dosage until I was off it completely after three months. An unwanted side effect of the medication was dramatic weight gain. I had gone from a UK size 6 to a size 18 in the time I had been in hospital. I tried hard to lose the weight but it wasn't easy. The drugs had affected my metabolism and it took a long time to lose weight; it's a journey I'm still on, as I write this book.

Melanie Burnell

Chapter Twenty

I vowed never to start a business again as it was the stress from that which had made me ill. It wasn't worth it; it's not like I had put in all that hard work and got ill but at least had something to show for it – a lasting legacy which I could pass on to my daughter in years to come. Instead I had made myself very ill with nothing to show for it.

However, a few weeks after my discharge from hospital, a lunch meeting with an old friend reignited my entrepreneurial spirit and I embarked on a new journey which was exciting and rewarding but without the stress as I learned to work smarter not harder.

I met Jean at a little café near to her art gallery in St Albans, Hertfordshire one sunny afternoon in August. Jean was a fellow business woman in the art industry who I'd been friends with and worked alongside for a number of years. I told her about my illness and my time in hospital. She was shocked and very understanding. "When you are ready" she said, "I have a business idea which I would like to work on with you."

I listened as she explained she wanted to develop an 'artists directory' website similar to the one I had done previously but much simpler for users to navigate and more up-to-date; a much higher spec version of my original site. Jean explained that there would be no time frame, no pressures. I could work on it at my own pace. She would fund it and we would go into business together as a partnership. She hired a web developer and I got to work designing logos for our new site. I couldn't help but throw myself into it. I knew from my first site what worked and what didn't and found the whole process of development much smoother and more enjoyable. There weren't the financial pressures involved or the immense pressure of having to launch within a certain time frame as before. I also knew much more about what I was doing this time round and I didn't feel the huge responsibility I had felt previously to my staff and hundreds of artists, reassuring them all that the transition from arts centre to website was the right thing to do and 'it will all be OK' when I was so up against it that deep down I was unsure myself.

Within weeks of launching it was already flying up the search engines as our artists and customers blogged, tweeted and shared their favourite artists and blog posts. It is now at the top of Google, something I never achieved with my last site. I learned how to harness the power of social media and use video marketing and digital technology, things that I didn't know a lot about when I launched my first site.

Chapter Twenty One

My old business partner never did close the business down; she kept the website going with our PA. We all arranged to meet for lunch a week after the meeting but they both cancelled and I haven't heard from them since.

I had no time to be annoyed though, as my site overtook hers in the Google search rankings and visitor numbers. I just focussed on making my new site the best it could be.

Within a few months we had over 700 artists from more than 40 countries and over 100,000 weekly art followers and the numbers are growing all the time. I feel like I am finally achieving what I set out to do all those years ago, and more.

Along the way I've learnt some hard lessons about trust, loyalty and the importance of looking after your mental health.

Epilogue

My journey through psychosis has taught me to appreciate the beautiful things in life like the sound of my daughter's laughter and the blossom on the trees. It's too easy to get caught up in striving for success and oversee the beauty in the world around us. I've learned not to abuse my mental health by working too hard. I remain grateful for the lessons my experience has taught me.

Writing this book has proved to be a very therapeutic experience. It's allowed others, not least of all my family, to gain a much deeper understanding of what I've been through and why I did what I did. I am so grateful to have survived and I cherish every day. I hope to help many others to see that there is light at the end of the tunnel and that you can come through the darkness into a much brighter world.

I would like to raise awareness of psychosis so that it can be identified and treated early. I want to use my experience to help others.

Melanie Burnell

Glossary

Psychosis

Causes

Each case of psychosis is different and the exact cause is not always entirely clear. Researchers believe genetic, biological and environmental factors all play a part. There are triggers like illnesses, stress, drug use, lack of sleep, genetic causes, brain chemicals, childhood experiences, birth complications and other environmental factors.

Among these factors the two main ones are drug abuse and extreme stress. In the case of extreme stress it can be as a result of a very traumatic experience however it's more likely to occur over many months and years where a person has mentally pushed themselves to their limit for a sustained period of time. Suffering from psychosis may be referred to as having a nervous breakdown - the mind simply has reached its limits and is damaged to a point where you can no longer do the basic things. Worse than that though is the awful tricks the mind plays on you, making it a very frightening and debilitating illness.

<u>Symptoms</u>

There are four main symptoms associated with psychosis. A sufferer may experience some or all of the following:

- hallucinations
- delusions
- confused and disturbed thoughts
- a lack of insight and self-awareness

Hallucinations

A hallucination is when you perceive something that does not exist in reality. Hallucinations can occur in all five of your senses.

- sight – someone with psychosis may see colours and shapes, or imaginary people or animals
- sounds – someone with psychosis may hear voices that are angry, unpleasant or sarcastic
- touch – a common psychotic hallucination is that insects are crawling on the skin
- smell – usually a strange or unpleasant smell
- taste – some people with psychosis have complained of having a constant unpleasant taste in their mouth

Delusion

A delusion is where you have an unshakeable belief in something implausible, bizarre or obviously untrue. Two examples of psychotic delusions are:

- paranoid delusion
- delusions of grandeur

Paranoid delusion

A person with psychosis will often believe an individual or organisation is making plans to hurt or kill them. This can lead to unusual behaviour. For example, a person with psychosis may refuse to be in the same room as a mobile phone because they believe they are mind-control devices.

Delusions of grandeur

A person with psychosis may have delusions of grandeur where they believe they have some imaginary power or authority. For example, they may think they are president of a country, or have the power to bring people back from the dead.

Confusion of thought

People with psychosis often have disturbed, confused and disrupted patterns of thought.

Signs of this include that:

- their speech may be rapid and constant
- the content of their speech may appear random; for example, they may switch from one topic to another mid- sentence
- their train of thought may suddenly stop, resulting in an abrupt pause in conversation or activity

Lack of insight

People experiencing psychosis are often totally unaware their behaviour is in any way strange, or their delusions or hallucinations could be imaginary.

They may be capable of recognising delusional or bizarre behaviour in others, but lack the self-awareness to recognise it in themselves. For example, a person with psychosis who is being treated in a psychiatric ward may complain that all of their fellow patients are mentally unwell while they are perfectly normal.

Early Warning Signs

These can be early warning signs of psychosis, which can lead to the more severe symptoms listed above if left untreated. You do not need to be suffering from them all to have psychosis. Also, some are also related to depression not just psychosis (there is a crossover of symptoms) The bold ones are more strongly associated with psychosis:

Feeling forgetful or far away

Feeling quiet or withdrawn

Feeling tense, afraid or anxious

Feeling as if my thoughts might be controlled

Feeling as if I'm being watched

Not feeling like eating

Feeling confused or puzzled

Having no interest in things

Feeling as if I'm being laughed at or talked about

Sleep has been unsettled

Feeling as if my thoughts might not be my own

Feeling unable to cope, difficulty managing every day tasks

Feeling depressed or low

Having difficulty concentrating

Getting transfixed by or preoccupied with 1 or 2 things

Also By Melanie Burnell

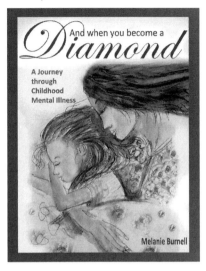

Follow one mother's journey to help her daughter
through a myriad of mental health issues which
appeared to surface suddenly and without warning.

Following a breakdown which had seen her incarcerated
in a psychiatric unit for three months suffering with psychosis, Melanie now thought all her troubles were behind
her. She had made a full recovery and life was good
again. Until, a year to the day, she was released from
hospital and a frightening turn of events saw her young
daughter fighting for her life after taking an overdose.
Suddenly her nightmare returned, only this time her
daughter was at the centre of it.

But why? She hadn't seemed troubled, had coped with
everything so well and seemed to be flourishing.

AVAILABLE ON AMAZON

30988108R00063

Printed in Great
Britain
by Amazon